Frederiksborg Museum

Guide Modern Collection

GUIDE
Frederiksborg Museum
Modern Collection

Text:
Steffen Heiberg
and Thorkild Kjærgaard
with contributions from
Anders Sode-Pedersen
English translation by
Joan F. Davidson
Cover illustration reproduced
from: Queen Margrethe II
by Andy Warhol (p. 123)
©Det Nationalhistoriske
Museum på Frederiksborg,
Denmark 1994

Layout: Ole Zøfting-Larsen
Production: F. Hendriksen's Eftf. A/S
ISBN 87–87237–55–5

Where no other indication
is given the works con-
cerned are oil on canvas.
The dimensions are given
in centimetres, height first.

Entrance to the Modern
Collection on the 3rd floor
is via the Entrance Hall
and Royal Staircase.
Tickets give access to the
whole museum.

The museum is open every day
May-September, 10 am–5 pm
October, 10 am–4 pm
November-March, 11 am–3 pm
April, 10 am–4 pm.

Contents

Introduction
Modern Collection

When Frederiksborg Museum was established in 1878 as a department of the Carlsberg Foundation, interest focused not only on the past, but also on contemporary times. The museum's statutes laid down that the historical collections should continually be brought up to date and supplemented with recent artistic representations, in painting and sculpture, of notable events and personalities.

The extension of the collections which has taken place in the 20th century has centred on portraits, but also includes historical representations in the broader sense, examples of applied art and other objects associated with historical personages and events.

The accessions have been acquired by means of purchase, commissioning or receipt of donations from individuals, committees and foundations. In a large number of cases, pictures of distinguished Danes have been painted at the request of the museum, e.g. the portraits of Vilhelm Thomsen, philologist; J. C. Christensen, politician; Valdemar Poulsen, engineer; Knud Rasmussen, Arctic explorer; Carl Nielsen, composer; Carl T. Dreyer, film-director; Niels Bohr, nuclear physicist; Bodil Ipsen, actress; A. P. Møller, ship-owner, and the writer Karen Blixen, to name but a few.

The royal portrait gallery in the Great Hall (Riddersalen) has been further extended, most recently with full-length portraits of Queen Margrethe II by Preben Hornung, in 1985, and the Prince Consort by the French painter Malel (1993).

Particular historical events have given rise to works being commissioned by the museum, e.g. the reunion of North Slesvig with Denmark in 1920, which was commemorated in the form of a picture-triad by the painter Hans Nikolaj Hansen. The reunion pictures, together with portraits of the North Slesvig politicians, form a natural conclusion to a section which begins with the Slesvig wars, and they have therefore been kept in the historical collection. The time of the German Occupation also gave rise to increased collecting-activity, which resulted e.g. in Georg Jacobsen's large group portrait of the Danish Freedom Council, and also a series of posthumous portraits of people from the resistance movement. The museum has moreover on some occasions taken the initiative to commission "history paintings", as in the case of Aksel Jørgensen's depiction of Christian X's meeting with Parliament on 9 May 1945, although this never became more than a sketch.

From 1990 onwards the museum has begun a more active and systematic collection of por-trait photographs, and these photographs, whether commissioned or acquired by other means, now enter the collections on an equal footing with other forms of portrait art.

The department for the 20th century is housed on the third floor of the King's wing (Kongefløjen), where in 1992–93 renovation was undertaken by the architect firm Fogh & Følner. The modern collection is presented in a contemporary exhibition-architecture with electric lighting and is different from the rest of the museum in that it is not displayed in the context of a furnished interior. In addition, new media have been introduced. With the provision of a small video-room and a larger area where films and slides can be shown, it has become possible to supplement the fixed displays in this new department with a changing range of historical and biographical films. The modern collection is arranged in chronological order, divided into thematic subsections. Its overall character is that of a portrait gallery where each individual picture marks a contribution and forms a memorial to a personage who has played a role in the history of Denmark. Portraits of individuals or groups are linked together by pictures with a more narrative content. This creates a total image which at different points reflects developments within politics, society, academic subjects, industry and culture. A former decision not to display representations of living persons other than royalty has been rescinded. Because of the multiplicity of artistic forms of expression in the 20th century the department presents a motley display. It includes a permanent core which is supplemented as time goes on with temporary displays appropriate to newly-acquired material.

Foto: Jens Frederiksen,

Plan of the Collection

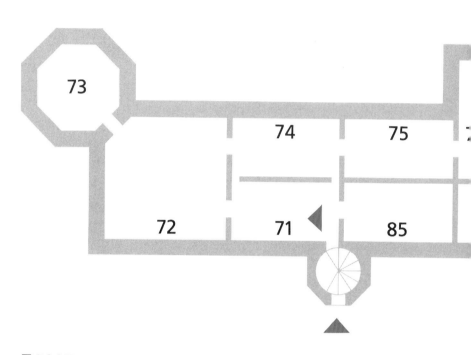

■ **ROOM**

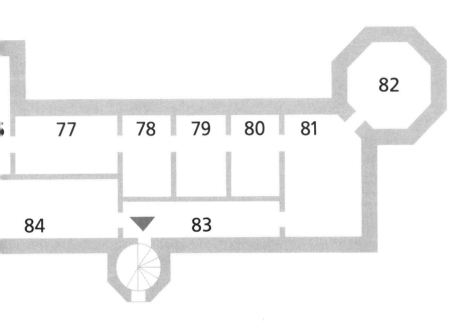

■ ROOM

71

Denmark at the beginning of the 20th century

Science and industry

Around the year 1900 Denmark was an agricultural country undergoing rapid change. A decisive factor was industrialization, which became a force to be reckoned with from the 1890s onwards. The blaze of electric light in P. S. Krøyer's painting *Industrialists* from 1903 gives an impression of the optimism which surrounded the expansion of industry. All was not perfect harmony, however. Erik Henningsen's painting *An Agitator* reflects the political agitation for better living-conditions for the working class.

A basic precondition for industrialization was scientific and technological development. Niels Bohr's epoch-making studies in nuclear physics gained him the Nobel prize in 1922. Among those who contributed to the practical applications of academic advances, mention can be made of I. W. Tegner, the railway engineer and Director General of the State Railways, of whom a bust, the work of his nephew Rudolf Tegner, can be seen. Credit for the expansion of the infrastructure is also due to Jørgen Fibiger, the harbour-building engineer, painted by Niels Hansen, and to N. C. Monberg, the major contractor, painted by N. V. Dorph. The latter artist also painted the founder of the East Asiatic Company, H. N. Andersen.

71

Industrialists

P. S. Krøyer. 1903–04.
115.5 × 184.5. (A 7348).

The scene is the Eastern Electricity Works in Copenhagen; a number of prominent figures in industry and engineering are present. Above, to the left, the commissioner and first owner of the painting, G. A. Hagemann (1842–1916), engineer, director of the Polytechnical University. On the floor, at the extreme left, is the General Director of the State Railways, I. W. Tegner (1832–1909) and brewer Carl Jacobsen (1842–1914) of Carlsberg. The figures further to the right include Philip Schou (1838–1922) from Royal Copenhagen Porcelain;

engineer Alexander Foss (1858–1925); the engineer and inventor Valdemar Poulsen (1869–1942), and Alfred Benzon, pharmaceutical manufacturer (1855–1932). The painting does not represent any actual event, but is a tribute to industry as the liberator of mankind.

An Agitator

Erik Henningsen. 1899.
23.5 × 33.5. (A 6645).

The scene is the Fælled Park (the Common) in Copenhagen, which after the "Battle on the Common" in 1872 became a centre for Social Democratic agitation. The speaker is possibly Frederik Borgbjerg (1866–1936), who later became Education Minister.

15

71

Niels Bohr

Otto Sievert. 1926.
100 × 70. (A 4057).

The nuclear physicist Niels
Bohr (1885–1962) began as
an experimental physicist,
but it was as a theoretician
that he revolutionized the
physical world picture. In
1913, after visiting Ernest
Rutherford in Cambridge,
he published his epoch-
making articles on the
structure of atoms. Nobel
prize 1922. In 1927 he
formulated the theory of
complementarity with im-
portant cognitive aspects.
Belonged to the team
which developed the atom
bomb in the USA during
the 2nd World War. In
1950, in an open letter to
the UN, Bohr warned
against the build-up of
nuclear weapons and made
a plea for cooperation
between the USA and the
USSR.

Jørgen Fibiger

Niels Hansen. 1919.
94.5 × 115.5. (A 7830).

The development of the ports on the west coast of Jutland in order to link Denmark more closely with world markets was an important task at the beginning of the 20th century. Hydraulic engineer Jørgen Fibiger (1867–1936) was a driving force in the construction of Hirtshals Harbour, completed in 1930, and of the technically demanding Hanstholm Harbour.

I. W. Tegner

Rudolph Tegner.
Bronze bust. 1899.
45.4 × 34 × 29.
(A 6925).

In 1867, after a military career, I. W. Tegner (1832–1909), became Senior Engineer of the Jutland-Funen railways. From 1889 to 1902 he was Director General of the State Railways. In his time the extent of the railway network in Denmark was multiplied many times over, and a number of important bridges, e.g. one over the Limfjord in North Jutland, as well as ferry-links, were brought into service.

71

N. C. Monberg

*N. V. Dorph. 1926.
72 × 58. (A 4477).*

N. C. Monberg (1856–1930) carried out a number of major building works, including harbour constructions, bridges and railway stations in Denmark and abroad. His greatest works in Denmark include the Goods Station in Copenhagen, the railway bridge over Mariager Fjord at Hadsund in Jutland and the canal at Hvide Sande on the North Sea coast.

Monberg's work contributed to establishing a basis on which Danish construction-firms were later to expand. His name lives on in the still-existing firm of Monberg & Thorsen, which was founded in 1919 by his son Axel Monberg, together with Ejnar Thorsen.

H. N. Andersen

N. V. Dorph. 1928.
68 × 56.5. (A 5579).

H. N. Andersen (1852–1937) was the son of a worker in the small town of Nakskov and ended his life in Copenhagen as director of Denmark's largest business concern, the East Asiatic Company, of which he himself was the founder. He was very attentive to the commercial and industrial opportunities inherent in the incipient globalisation of the economy, and exploited them adroitly to his own advantage and that of Denmark. He cultivated people of strong will and individuality, as did a number of his contemporaries; in consequence mass democracy had little appeal to him. The fairytale style of Andersen's career shows that the "American Dream" could also come true in the old European world.

72

Political change and votes for women

Politics 1900–1920

The early decades of the 20th century were a period of breakthrough for democracy. Changes in the political system in Denmark, introduced in 1901, brought parliamentary constitutional practice, with Cabinet responsibility, into being, and the constitution of 1915 gave women the right to vote. A selection of drawings show distinguished female politicians and writers; they include Herluf Jensenius's drawing of the social democrat Nina Bang and Aage Roose's portrait of the writer Thit Jensen. The new constitution, with the support of all the political parties, was carried through by C. T. Zahle's *Radikale Venstre* [social-liberal] government; the Cabinet members can be seen on Julius Paulsen's group picture.

In 1908 democracy suffered damage when frauds were disclosed for which P. A. Alberti (Minister of Justice) was responsible. He had shortly before been painted in ministerial uniform by Paul Fischer. Ludvig Find painted Jens Jensen, the first social democratic mayor of Copenhagen, while J. F. Willumsen produced a striking portrait of the Copenhagen councillor Gustav Philipsen.

One of the distinctive profiles in politics was that of social-liberal Ove Rode, who as Minister of the Interior during the 1st World War carried

Nina Bang

Herluf Jensenius. Indian ink, black chalk, white body colour.
1924. 16.5 × 30. (A 8585).

Nina Bang (1866–1928), was a historian, social democrat, and Education Minister in the first Social Democratic government, in 1924. Denmark's first woman minister. In spite of her great significance for equality of women in Denmark, she herself was not interested in feminism as such but considered women's problems as an element in the overall political conflict.

72

out comprehensive economic adjustments to secure the supply of fuel and foodstuffs to the population. This could not prevent social and political tensions from growing, however. Indignation over the prevailing social conditions was expressed in the drawings of Anton Hansen. A private initiative aimed at improving social conditions was the Christmas Seal Homes, which were financed from income from the sale, from 1904 onwards, of seals for Christmas mail. A bust, the work of C. Arvesen, shows the originator of the Christmas seals, Postmaster Einer Holbøll (1865–1927).

A decisive factor in the improvement of living conditions was the progress of medical knowledge. P. S. Krøyer painted the light-treatment hall at the Finsen Institute, which became a symbol of modern medical science.

Thit Jensen

Aage Roose. Black chalk. 32.5 × 26.5. (A 7450).

Thit Jensen (1876–1957) wrote a series of much-read historical novels. She provoked dispute over her intrepid campaign to improve women's conditions by means of "planned motherhood". Her spiritualistic representations also excited attention. She is depicted, characteristically, giving a lecture.

C. T. Zahle

Herman Vedel. Oil on plywood. c. 1916 44 × 32. (A 6889).

From the days of his youth onwards Prime Minister C. T. Zahle (1866–1946) was an ardent defender of the weaker members of society. In 1901 he wrote an impassioned book about the Danish smallholder which became normative for the social policies of the *Radikale Venstre* [social-liberal] party. Sketch for the Constitution painting in the Parliament wing of Christiansborg Palace 1916–17.

23

72

A meeting of Zahle's Cabinet during the First World War

Julius Paulsen. 1916–17. 175 × 211. (A 2820).

C. T. Zahle formed his second government in June 1913 in order to carry through the new constitution, which was signed on 5 June 1915. By then the First World War had broken out, in August 1914, rendering a change of government impossible. The government, which had come to power as a transitional one, was permitted to remain until 1920, and became one of the longest-lasting governments ever. The government's five dominant members – apart from its head, C. T. Zahle (1866–1946), who is seen in the centre – were Finance Minister Edvard Brandes (1847–1931), Defence Minister P. Munch (1870–1948), Foreign Minister Erik Scavenius (1877–1962), and Minister of the Interior Ove Rode (1867–1933). The three last-mentioned are to the right of the Prime Minister. The painting was commissioned by the financier and art collector H. Heilbuth, who in 1923 donated it to Frederiksborg Museum.

72

J. C. Christensen

Herman Vedel. c. 1916.
64 × 48.5. (A 6924).

J. C. Christensen (1856–1930), a teacher in Jutland, was elected Member of Parliament for the *Venstre* [liberal] party in 1890. Became Prime Minister in 1905, the first ordinary citizen to occupy this post. One of the most prominent Danish politicians of the 20th century. Sketch for the Constitution painting at Christiansborg Palace 1916–17.

P. A. Alberti

Paul Fischer. 1906.
28.2 × 20.2. (A 8798).

P. A. Alberti (1851–1932) belonged to the conservative wing of the *Venstre* [liberal] party. Became Minister of Justice in 1901. Carried through the law on abolition of public

prostitution in 1906. Prolonged and aggressive attacks on his conduct in office led in 1908 to his confession to defrauding a savings bank of more than 8 million kroner. He was condemned to eight years imprisonment for his crimes.

Anarchist

Anton Hansen. Water-colour, Indian ink, ink and pencil. 1916. 26.7×22.3. (A 8744).

In 1916–17 Anton Hansen made a series of drawings for the newspaper *Ekstra Bladet*, taking up the cudgels, in a socialist stance, against the upper class, the Church, the army, the police, the judiciary and war-speculators. This drawing was published on 18 December 1916 with the text "Twenty days' im-prisonment for the most

brazen war-profiteering – three years' jail for stealing a pair of old boots – God bless our beloved Father-land!!"

72

The Light Room in the Finsen Institute

P. S. Krøyer. Pastel. 1903. 113 × 185. (A 8794).

The doctor Niels Finsen (1860–1904), Nobel prize-winner 1903, discovered the healing effect of ultra-violet light and in 1900 established a light-treatment institute for healing tuberculosis of the skin (lupus). The institute was set up in a former riding-school. A number of lead-ing figures in medical research can be seen grouped around Niels Finsen. The man in the dark suit immediately to the right of Finsen is the director of the Poly-technical University, G. A. Hagemann (1842–1916), who gave Finsen economic support.

Niels Finsen

C. Wentorf. 1904–06.
117 × 76. (A 1799).

In C. Wentorf's posthumous
picture, Niels Finsen is
depicted in the white coat
which in those years
became the symbol of
progress in terms of medi-
cine and hygiene in the
hospital system. Painted at
the request of Frederiks-
borg Museum.

72

The International Commission on the Plebiscites in Slesvig

Harald Slott-Møller. 1919.
42.1 x 79.9. (A 8194).

The most significant event of the period was the reunion of North Slesvig with Denmark in 1920. Harald Slott-Møller painted the International Commission which according to the terms of the Versailles peace treaty supervised the arrangements for plebiscites on the future allegiance of Slesvig. From the left, Oscar von Sydow, later Prime Minister of Sweden; Thomas Heftye, former Defence Minister of Norway; Sir Charles Mar-

ling, British Ambassador to Denmark, and Paul Claudel, the poet, French Ambassador to Denmark. At the end of the table is the Commission's secretary. The Commission's meeting-place was Flensburg: a view of it is visible in the background. Sketch of a painting in the Parliament wing of Christiansborg Palace.

Klaus Berntsen

Herman Vedel. c. 1916.
52 × 44. (A 6891).

Klaus Berntsen (1844–1927) represented the Assens constituency for the *Venstre* [liberal] party from 1886–1926. Prime Minister and Defence Minister 1910–13. He was the driving force behind the preparation of the new constitution, although it in fact fell to C. T. Zahle to sign it.

Gustav Philipsen

J. F. Willumsen. 1919.
61.5 × 50.5. (A 4007).

Both as a publisher and as a politician, Gustav Philipsen (1853–1925), a leading Copenhagen Councillor, had many contacts with artists and intellectuals. Preparatory work for a double portrait with Mayor Jacob Marstrand in Copenhagen Town Hall. Willumsen was asked to paint this official portrait in the hope that it would be more animated than portraits of previous mayors. "They were all men in black coats who could just as well have been undertakers."

73

Greenland

At the beginning of the century Greenland was a Danish colony, closed to the rest of the world. The scientific investigation of the huge Arctic island intensified in 1902–04 with the "Literary Expedition", which had the task of investigating the culture and life-style of the people of North-West Greenland. The expedition was led by L. Mylius Erichsen; the participants included the very young Knud Rasmussen and his childhood friend Jørgen Brønlund. During a further expedition in 1906–08, the "Denmark Expedition", Mylius Erichsen and Jørgen Brønlund, along with a third participant, First-Lieutenant N. P. Høeg Hagen, lost their lives in dramatic circumstances in northern Greenland. There is a painted plaster-group of the expedition participants who perished. In the show case Brønlund's watch and diary, found later, are displayed along with a position-finding instrument used by the "Denmark Expedition". There are two paintings of Knud Rasmussen, an early portrait by Eigil Schwab, and one painted at the request of Frederiksborg Museum by Herman Vedel. Other prominent Greenland researchers were Lauge Koch, Ejnar Mikkelsen and Peter Freuchen.
In 1921, 200 years after Hans Egede's arrival in Greenland, Christian X undertook a journey to

73

the northern territorial possessions of his country. The journey was part of Denmark's efforts to maintain its sovereignty over Greenland, contested by Norway. It was not until 1933, after a ruling by the International Court of Justice in the Hague, that Norway recognized Denmark's full sovereignty over Greenland. In the wake of this international recognition, Greenland has gradually opened up and commercial and social life there has become modernized.

The "Denmark Expedition" to North-East Greenland, 1906–08

Holger Wederkinch.
Plaster group.
Painted by
Søren Kongstrand.
49 × 43. (A 8199).

The group shows the three people who lost their lives during the "Denmark Expedition". In front, Jørgen Brønlund (1877–1907), behind, Mylius Erichsen (1872–1907), who with his right hand is supporting the falling Brønlund. At the back, N. P. Høeg Hagen (1877–1907). Competition piece, not used, for a monument to the "Denmark Expedition".

Knud Rasmussen

*Herman Vedel. 1928.
79 × 65.2. (A 4326).*

Knud Rasmussen (1879–
1933) was of both Danish
and Greenland descent.
His seven "Thule Expedi-
tions" to North-East
Greenland, Arctic Canada
and Alaska provided the
foundations for research
into the culture and living-
conditions of the polar
Eskimo. He fashioned his
knowledge into popular
and scientific writing on a
large scale, and translated
Eskimo legends and songs.
Depicted in a reindeer
anorak with a dog-whip in
his hand.

J. P. Koch

*Achton Friis. Black chalk.
1907. 47 × 38. (A 4181).*

Officer J. P. Koch (1870–
1928) participated in the
"Denmark Expedition" as
cartographer. Drawn by
another expedition-
member, the artist Achton
Friis, who also drew a
number of the other mem-
bers of the expedition.

35

73

Christian X at the people's gathering in Juliedalen near Jakobshavn (Ilulissat) on 14 July 1921

Laurits Tuxen. Oil on damask. 1921.
86 × 112. (A 2786).

In the summer of 1921 Christian X visited the northern parts of his kingdom, Greenland and Iceland. Behind the King are Queen Alexandrine and Crown Prince Frederik (IX). Laurits Tuxen took part in the journey as painter-of-record.

Peter Freuchen

Philippe Halsman.
Photograph. 1957.
34.3 × 27.1. (F 85).

Peter Freuchen (1886–
1957), participant in the
"Denmark Expedition",
1906–08. Together with
Knud Rasmussen he
founded the trading
station in Thule in 1910.
Author of a number
of novels, memoirs and
studies in cultural
geography. Wrote the
autobiography *Adventures*
in the Arctic (1960).

Lauge Koch

Johannes Glob. 1933.
92 × 81. (A 8195).

The geologist Lauge Koch
(1892–1964) completed the
mapping of the north
coast of Greenland in
1920–23. In the years
1931–34 he led an expedi-
tion to Christian X's Land
with cartographers, geolo-
gists, zoologists, botanists
and archaeologists as
members. During this ex-
pedition aeroplanes were
used for the first time in
Greenland.

74

New and old approaches

Literature and art
1900–1920

A distinctive element in literature at the beginning of the century was interest in home background and in the life of the common people. Inspiration from local background was combined in Johannes V. Jensen's work with optimism about the technological future, and in the work of Martin Andersen Nexø with a socialistic Utopia. Jeppe Aakjær gave writing about his native soil a social significance, e.g. in the novel *Vredens Børn* (The Children of Wrath, 1904) about the plight of the day-labourer. Jeppe Aakjær also became known for his lyrical-narrative interpretations of the attitudes and lives of farming people in Jutland. Aakjær was painted by Kristen Bjerre. A parallel to Aakjær was Johan Skjoldborg, the small-holder-poet, who is depicted in a water-colour by Johannes Nielsen.

In 1922 Herman Vedel painted the ageing Georg Brandes, who confirmed his international reputation with biographies of a number of major figures in world history: Voltaire, Shakespeare, Caesar, Goethe and others. Within architecture the national-romantic trend was dominant. One of the main examples was Copenhagen Town Hall, built around the turn of the century. The architect Martin Nyrop is depicted on the roof of the Town Hall together with his clerk of works, Emil Jørgensen. P. V.

74

Jensen Klint, the architect of the Grundtvig Church in Copenhagen, continued in the tradition of Nyrop. The bust of him is by Johannes C. Bjerg, who along with Kai Nielsen was prominent among the sculptors of the period. In the first decade of the century Danish art ranged from the internationally-orientated J. F. Willumsen to the unobtrusive Vilhelm Hammershøi, who was primarily interested in domestic themes. In the cathedrals in Viborg and Lund Joakim Skovgaard created his biblical representations. His brother Niels Skovgaard was a master of design and applied art, as was Thorvald Bindesbøll. Poul S. Christiansen, whose imposing bust in bog oak is by Jens Lund, was one of the *Fynboerne* (a group of artists from Funen) who described the Danish landscape and ordinary rural life. Among the last portrait-painters of the old school were Herman Vedel and Julius Paulsen, who were both commissioned to paint portraits by Frederiksborg Museum.

With the modernist breakthrough around 1910, interest shifted from theme to style. Among the pioneers were Harald Giersing, William Scharff, Olaf Rude and Vilhelm Lundstrøm. Carl Jensen, whose portrait was painted by Scharff, was an artist specialising in political satire. He caricatured three of his friends – Svend Johansen, Vilhelm Lundstrøm and Karl Larsen. A place apart is occupied by the artist Robert Storm Petersen (Storm P.); with subtle humour and a fine sense of social justice, using a naive cartoon style, he captured everyday life and miserable contemporary characters.

The first decade of the century saw the breakthrough of the film. In Denmark Ole Olsen established one of the world's first film companies, still in existence now, *Nordisk Film*. The reputation of Danish films was based especially on one of the major stars of the silent screen, a genius at mime, Asta Nielsen. One of the distinguished theatre personalities of the time was Betty Nansen, who in her own theatre produced and performed a literary repertoire in which topical social and moral issues were raised. The dominant figure in Danish music was the composer Carl Nielsen, who distinguished himself at the beginning of the century with the operas *Saul and David* (1902) and *Masquerade* (1904). He did not win national recognition until around 1915, however. The person responsible for the building up of the state broadcasting company, now *Danmarks Radio*, was the opera singer Emil Holm. The prominent position always accorded to education and cultural matters in Danish broadcasting is due to a great extent to Emil Holm's grasp of the pedagogic possibilities of the medium.

74

Johannes V. Jensen

Ludvig Find. 1927.
74.4 × 64. (A 4060).

Far-flung travels as a correspondent for the newspapers *Politiken* and *Social-Demokraten* turned Johannes V. Jensen (1873–1950) into a believer in progress and unconditional admirer of America's dynamic technical society. His main work, *The Long Journey* is a myth about the white man's conquest of the world and is based on a Social-Darwinist view of society. Among his other works were the novel *Fall of the King* and a number of poems. Nobel prize 1944. Painted at the request of Frederiksborg Museum.

Martin Andersen Nexø

August Tørsleff. 1913.
112 × 95. (A 2773).

Martin Andersen Nexø (1869–1954) grew up on the island of Bornholm in straitened circumstances and became a convinced socialist at an early age. His breakthrough came with the novel *Pelle the Conqueror* (1906–10), a social-democratic version of the classic Danish *Bildungsroman*. The novel *Ditte* (1917–21) expressed social indignation even more strongly. From the 1920s onwards he declared solidarity with the Soviet state, which he defended in all situations. On the occasion of the first hanging of the portrait, in 1922, the columnist "Ærbødigst" (Viggo Barfoed) in the conservative newspaper *BT* wrote a brief poem commenting on the irony of celebrating a leninist in the National Portrait Gallery, usually so strongly connected with monarchy.

74

Harald Kidde

Sigurd Swane. 1909.
82.7 × 65. (A 7546).

The writings of Harald
Kidde (1878–1918) never
reached a large public. A
distinguishing feature of
the melancholy and reli-
giously speculative novels
Helten (1912) and *Jernet*
(1918) is their stylistic ex-
perimentation, which has
been compared to that of
James Joyce's later novel
Ulysses (1922). Swane's
portrait of Kidde in a
forest landscape is in-
fluenced by the free painting style of the Impres-
sionists and makes use of
the pure strong colours
which Swane had encoun-
tered in Paris immediately
before.

Helge Rode

Edvard Munch. Pastel.
1891. 80.4 × 54. (A 7896).

The poetry of Helge Rode
(1870–1937) was intro-
verted and full of emotion
– a reaction against the
controversial naturalism
for which Georg Brandes
had campaigned. Edvard
Munch's delicate portrait-
sketch of the young poet
smoking his pipe was
made in Copenhagen in
the year of Helge Rode's
debut, 1891.

74

Julius Paulsen

Victor Isbrand. 1932.
34.2×27. (A 8685).

As a portrait-painter Julius
Paulsen (1860–1940) was
capable of combining
distinct characteristics with
fine colouring, as in the
group-portrait of Zahle's
Cabinet. Julius Paulsen also
achieved significance as a
landscape artist, clearly
influenced by French
open-air painting. Victor
Isbrand's portrait with its
refined reflections of light
in the spectacles appears
to have been influenced by
Paulsen's own self-portrait
from 1912 in the collection
of portraits at the Royal
Academy of Arts in
Charlottenborg.

P. V. Jensen-Klint

Johannes C. Bjerg.
Granite bust. 1916–17.
59.5 × 59.5 × 37.5. (A 7156).

The most important architectural achievements of P. V. Jensen-Klint (1853–1930) lay in the field of churchbuilding. A competition for a memorial to N. F. S. Grundtvig, set up in 1912, resulted in the construction of Jensen-Klint's magnified village church, the Grundtvig Church in Bispebjerg, Copenhagen, in 1921–40. Johannes C. Bjerg's bust of the architect's distinctive face, with his particular shape of beard, is sculpted in polished grey-black granite, 1916–17.

74

Kai Nielsen

Arne Lofthus. Fresco. 1915. 66 × 51. (A 4006).

The sculptor Kai Nielsen (1882–1924) in his short life created a number of exuberant female figures, characteristic portrait-busts and statues, and public monuments such as the memorial stone for Mylius Erichsen at Langelinie in Copenhagen, *Ymerbrønden* in Faaborg, Funen, and the decoration of Blågårds Plads in Copenhagen in 1912–16. The Norwegian-born painter Arne Lofthus, who had collaborated with Joakim Skovgaard on the decoration of Viborg Cathedral and developed a great interest in the fresco technique, created this delicate portrait of Kai Nielsen using that technique.

Three avant-garde painters

Carl Jensen. Indian ink and pencil. 1920. 34.2 × 25.8. (A 8887).

Carl Jensen's caricature of his three fellow-artists Svend Johansen (1890–1970), Vilhelm Lundstrøm (1893–1950) and Karl Larsen (1897–1977) was published in the newspaper *Ekstra Bladet* on 31 December 1920 on the occasion of the opening of *Den frie Udstilling* in Copenhagen. They belonged to the circle around the art-magazine *Klingen*, which was issued from 1917 to 1921 and was a mouthpiece for cubism.

74

Emil Holm

Herman Vedel. 1933.
120×100. (A 7029).

In 1925, after a career in Denmark and Germany as a dramatic bass singer, Emil Holm (1867–1950) became director of the newly established state broadcasting company. The prominent position accorded to education and cultural matters in Danish broadcasting since then is due to a great extent to Emil Holm's grasp of the pedagogic possibilities of the medium. He was also behind the creation of a radio-symphony orchestra of international standard. Herman Vedel's portrait of the singer, looking at us through a monocle, was described by the leftish writer and architect Poul Henningsen as "conservative art as it is and should be".

Kræsten Iversen

Johannes C. Bjerg.
Teak-wood bust. 1920.
43 × 20.2 × 20. (A 8730).

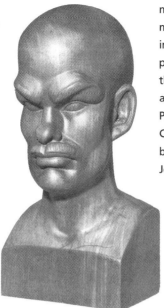

Kræsten Iversen (1886–1955) was one of the few artists of his time who painted in the monumental style, and he was commissioned to carry out major decorative works, including the ceiling-paintings in the building of the Academy of Sciences and Letters and in the Parliament building at Christiansborg. The teak bust is by his friend Johannes C. Bjerg.

Carl Nielsen

Julius Paulsen. 1931.
86 × 66. (A 4559).

The composer Carl Nielsen (1865–1931) has influenced Danish musical life to a greater extent than anyone else in the 20th century. His works include six symphonies, operas, chamber music and choral pieces; above all, however, it is because of his contribution to the Danish song tradition that he is known and loved in Denmark. Julius Paulsen's portrait was completed for the Frederiksborg Museum in the year of the composer's death.

die Asta
H.B. -39.

Asta Nielsen

Hans Bendix. Black chalk. 1939. 36.9 × 21.1. (A 12634).

Asta Nielsen (1881–1972), was one of the major stars of the silent screen for more than twenty years. She acted in around 70 films, many of them in Germany, where she became known as *"Die Asta"*. Hans Bendix has captured her dark, distinctive beauty with her expressive eyes, from around the time her career came to an end.

Betty Nansen

Anders Zorn. Etching. 1905. 24.5 × 17.

This etching by the famous Swedish artist Anders Zorn shows the actress Betty Nansen, née Müller (1873–1943) as a typical beauty from *la belle époque*. The figure at the window is given shape with Zorn's characteristic rapid parallel strokes. After her debut in 1893 Betty Nansen developed her talents in a series of celebrated roles at the Dagmar Theatre and became the most outstanding actress of her time.

75

Politics and science

The restrictive policies in force during the First World War were succeeded in the 1920s by a liberal economic policy. The world crisis and mass unemployment after 1929 brought about a new change, and under the leadership of the Social Democrats and the *Radikale Venstre* [social-liberals] a comprehensive policy of economic control was put into practice.

The main spokesman for the liberalism of the twenties was the leader of the *Venstre* [liberal] party, Thomas Madsen-Mygdal (1876–1943), Prime Minister 1926–29. The dominant political figure in the thirties was the Social Democratic leader Thorvald Stauning, who in time became a national father-figure. Stauning was painted in 1929, when he became Prime Minister for the second time. The aim of Stauning's Government to promote social levelling and stability found expression in the social reform of 1933, principally designed by the Minister of Social Affairs K. K. Steincke. The Foreign Minister was P. Munch, who tried, well into the thirties, to keep Denmark out of European conflicts by actively supporting the League of Nations and passively adapting to the growth of power in Hitler's Germany, to the south. Internally Nazism was also a political and moral threat. The non-democratic opposition was represented by, among others, the

75

Danish Nazi Party (DNSAP). The leader of the party, Fritz Clausen (1893–1947), a doctor, is caricatured by Herluf Bidstrup. Among the many distinguished scientists of the time were the internationally-known cancer researcher Albert Fischer, who is portrayed on a relief by Anne Marie Carl Nielsen. Mogens Lorentzen painted his father, the doctor Carl Lorentzen, who contributed to organizing the campaign against tuberculosis. In addition there is a portrait of Thorvald Madsen, who in the 1920s developed a vaccine against diphtheria. The zoologist and freshwater biologist C. Wesenberg-Lund was painted in his laboratory.

Thorvald Stauning

Heinrich Dohm. 1929. 94 × 75.5. (A 4545).

The cigar sorter Thorvald Stauning (1873–1942) became the Social Democrat leader in 1910. In 1924 he formed the country's first Social-Democratic govern-ment and from 1929–40 he led a coalition govern-ment with the *Radikale Venstre* [social-liberal] party. The policy of economic control stemming from the world economic crisis was used as a tool for social reform. On his death, Johannes V. Jensen wrote "He grew from the very marrow of the nation. He took the interests of the country as his own. Who is there now who can take up the succession?"

K. K. Steincke

Ivan Opffer. Red chalk. 1931. 41×27. (A 8016).

K. K. Steincke (1880–1963) was among the first academics who joined the Social Democratic party. As Minister of Social Affairs he was the chief figure behind the social reform of 1933, which was the basis of Danish social policy until 1976. With his tendency towards paradoxal and provocative statements, Steincke was at times controversial.

P. Munch

Gustav Østerberg. Pencil and Indian ink. 1920s. 17×10.7. (A 12975).

In 1905 the historian P. Munch (1870–1948) helped found the *Radikale Venstre* [social-liberal] party, whose ideals of social solidarity he communicated to several generations of school-pupils through his text-books in history and civics. As Foreign Minister from 1929 to 1940 he practised with regard to Germany a pragmatic policy of adaptation, which was strongly criticized after 9 April 1940. The drawing, probably from the end of the 1920s, shows P. Munch, aloof, in a characteristic posture, speaking in Parliament.

75

H. Hauch

Olaf Rude. 1947.
100 × 82.5. (A 7332).

In the period between the wars, trade organizations engaged in increasingly close cooperation with the Government on economic and social policy. Cooperation with the agricultural organizations was particularly important. H. Hauch (1876–1957), who was an influential member of the *Venstre* [liberal] party and president of the Agricultural Council from 1933, played an important part in this. The painting was a gift from the agricultural societies to Hauch on his 70th birthday. It was decided that after Hauch's death the portrait should go to Frederiksborg Museum, and for that reason the museum's director was allowed to choose the artist.

Albert Fischer

Anne Marie Carl Nielsen.
Bronze relief. 1928.
Diameter 43.5. (A 8612).

Dr. Albert Fischer (1891–1956) was an international authority on cell physiology and cancer research. The establishment of the Carlsberg Foundation's Biological Institute in 1932 made it possible for him to continue his research in Denmark; he was director of the Institute until his death.

Carl Lorentzen

Mogens Lorentzen.
Oil on paste-board. 1933.
100 × 70. (A 7021).

Carl Lorentzen (1860–1932) worked for the setting up of tuberculosis sanatoria and was associated with the establishment of the National Society for the Campaign against Tuberculosis. This rapidly painted expressionist portrait is by his son, Mogens Lorentzen, who was a poet as well as a painter, art critic, actor and scenographer.

75

Thorvald Madsen

Herman Vedel. 1933–34.
85 × 68.5. (A 4788).

As director of the Serum Institute 1910–40, Dr. Thorvald Madsen (1870–1957) made a significant contribution to the international standardization of medical products. He was at the forefront of international aid during the 1st World War and – along with Fridtjof Nansen – in Russia after the revolution in 1917. After the 2nd World War he became a driving force in the UN children's organization UNICEF.

Fritz Clausen

Herluf Bidstrup. Indian ink and pencil. 1939.
31.5 × 28.6. (A 13601).

Fritz Clausen (1893–1947) was one of the founders of the Danish National Socialist Workers' Party (DNSAP) and its leader from 1933. Member of Parliament 1939–45. His corpulent figure made him an easy target for opponents and cartoonists. Herluf Bidstrup drew him in Nazi uniform for the newspaper *Social-Demokraten* on 4 January 1939, when he had been fined 200 kroner for slanderous statements about the Minister of Justice.

C. Wesenberg-Lund

Johannes Glob. 1938.
93 × 108. (A 7286).

The freshwater laboratory in which zoologist Wesenberg-Lund (1867–1955) worked still exists today; it is situated in Hillerød opposite Frederiksborg Castle. From there he produced a series of ground-breaking academic studies on insect life in fresh water. In addition Wesenberg-Lund made significant contributions to the cause of nature-protection and as a popular scientific writer. Made honorary citizen of Hillerød in 1947. The portrait is a gift from the subject, whose colleagues had presented it to him for his 70th birthday. The drawing in the background is from a book (1744) by the Swiss zoologist A. Trembley, and shows the freshwater polyp *Hydra*.

76

Tradition and intellectual leftism 1920–1940

The horrors of the 1st World War and inspiration from the Russian Revolution led to a re-evaluation of traditional social and cultural values. Examples reflecting this are Tom Kristensen's expressionist writing and Otto Gelsted's poetry. In contrast to the faith in the future expressed by Gelsted and Tom Kristensen, Jacob Paludan's novels reflect cultural pessimism, rootlessness and hostility to what, even as early as the 1920s, he considered to be Americanization of European culture. The humanist and cultural-radical Paul la Cour had significance both as a poet and as a critic. Desire for democratic aesthetic principles formed the basis for Poul Henningsen's work as an architect, cultural polemicist and writer. Poul Henningsen (known as PH) was one of the first to discern the possibilities of theatrical revue as a cultural-critical medium. A number of his texts were written for Liva Weel, who can be seen in Henry Heerup's portrait from 1945.

The theatre was dominated by Poul Reumert and Bodil Ipsen, who each separately and in interplay worked to keep the standard of dramatic performance at a high level for more than fifty years. Ivan Opffer drew the internationally renowned tenor Lauritz Melchior. A controversial clash with traditional national

76

values reached expression in Erik Arup's unfinished History of Denmark (1925–55). Arup was painted by his kindred-spirit Aksel Jørgensen. The belief in technological and social progress which formed the basis of Arup's History of Denmark also found expression in the renovation of the National Museum in the 1930s, during which emphasis was placed on phases of development. The restyling of the museum was spearheaded by the historian Mouritz Mackeprang, director of the museum from 1922 to 1938.

Jacob Paludan

Olaf Rude. 1946.
106.6 × 85.5. (A 7288).

Jacob Paludan (1896–1975) was one of the most important Danish novelists of the 20th century. A characteristic element of his writing is scepticism about the mentality of modern American society. His chief work, *Jørgen Stein* (1931), is a depiction of the ending of a cultural epoch caused by the 1st World War.

Liva Weel

Henry Heerup. 1945.
60 × 61. (A 8910).

Liva Weel (1897–1952)
made her name on the
stage in the Copenhagen
revues during the 20s.
In the 30s and 40s she
worked successfully
together with Poul
Henningsen, who wrote a
number of songs for her.
Heerup's portrait comes
from that period; its
simple lines and bold
colouring capture the
essence of her personality.

Paul la Cour

Preben Wilmann. 1922.
94 × 58. (A 8145).

Paul la Cour (1902–56)
made his debut as a poet
in 1922. In the course of
his life he produced poems,
novels and art criticism.
As a poet and art-critic he
was much engaged with
the relation between form
and content. In the 50s
he became involved with
international aid work.
Preben Wilmann's cubist
portrait of the 20-year-old
la Cour was painted in the
year of his debut.

76

Bodil Ipsen

Herman Vedel. Oil on cardboard. Probably 1930s. 40.7 × 33.3. (A 8134).

The actress Bodil Ipsen (1889–1964) was one of the most important figures in the Danish theatre in the first half of the 20th century. With her versatile talents she created a number of renowned stage roles, including Nora in Henrik Ibsen's *A Doll's House*. On the radio her expressive voice came into its own. She also worked as a theatre and film director. Herman Vedel's delicate and poetic portrait-sketch was probably made in the 30s.

Poul Reumert

G. F. Clement. 1928.
83.5 × 69. (A 4272).

Poul Reumert (1883–1968) was a major theatre perso- nality, known especially for his character roles in the Royal Theatre in Copen- hagen. Radio, records, and later TV made his voice familiar throughout the whole country. Clement's portrait shows the dark- haired temperamental actor at the age of 45.

76

Vilhelm Andersen

Herman Vedel. 1943.
156 × 92.5. (A 6716).

Vilhelm Andersen (1864–
1953) was a literary
historian who grew up in a
rectory in central Sealand.
Polemically opposed to
cosmopolitan attitudes, he
laid stress on national roots
as a conditioning force of
intellectual life. His belief
in the vital power of
Danish culture found ex-
pression in a major four-
volume illustrated history
of Danish literature
(1924–34), prepared in
cooperation with Carl
S. Petersen.

Sophus Claussen

Death mask. 1931.
26.5 × 19 × 17. (A 6732).

The poet Sophus Claussen
(1865–1931) became known
around 1890; after a long
relatively unproductive
period his poetry reached a
second peak in the 1920s.
His distinctive physiog-
nomy, with a vigorous
mane of hair and pointed
beard, retained its
demonic strength in the
death mask, which was
made by Anne Marie Carl
Nielsen, sculptor, and
P. Ferdinandsen, plasterer.

Erik Arup

Aksel Jørgensen. 1928.
63.6 × 48. (A 7349).

Erik Arup (1876–1951),
historian, professor at
Copenhagen University
from 1916. Worked for the
following 30 years on his –
never finished – history of
Denmark, which takes the
farmer's work with Den-
mark's soil as its central
theme. His history of Denmark was a literary master-
piece. The painting is a
preliminary work for a
group picture showing
Arup together with other
professors.

76

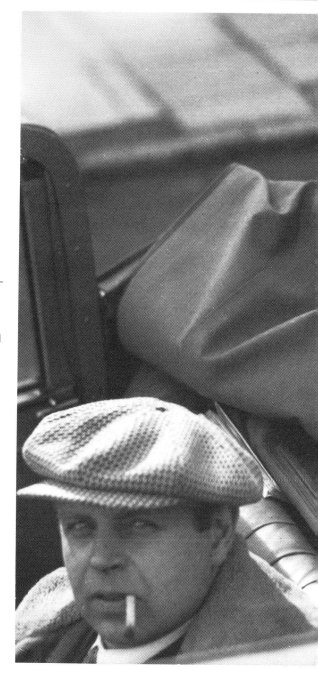

Three Culture Radicals

Herbert Davidsen. 1932.
Photograph. 29.8 × 36.9.

The architect, writer, social commentator and lamp-designer Poul Henningsen (PH) (1894–1967) played a dominant role in cultural and social debate in Denmark for almost half a century. Here he is seen together with two of his friends, the painter Svend Johansen (1890–1970) and the writer Otto Gelsted (1888–1968). The latter was frequent contributor to Poul Henningsen's magazine *Kritisk Revy* (1926–28) and was also a writer of theatre-revues in cooperation with PH.

76

R. Broby-Johansen

Hans Lollesgaard. Lithographic chalk and white body colour. 1950. 26.1 × 20.4. (A 13447).

The first published work of the writer R. Broby-Johansen (1900–1987) was a collection of poems, *Blod* (Blood) which was confiscated the day after publication, for blasphemy and pornography. A prominent figure in the far left in the 30s, from the early 40s he was known for his books about art. Lollesgaard's drawing was published in *Social-Demokraten* in 1950 on the occasion of Broby-Johansen's 50th birthday.

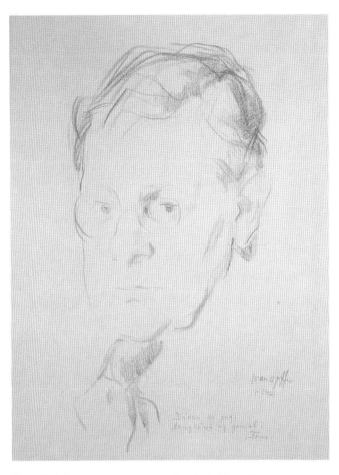

Tom Kristensen

*Ivan Opffer. Red chalk.
1924. 33 × 17. (A 7989).*

Tom Kristensen (1893–1974) had his first collection of poems published in 1920. In his youth he was absorbed in nihilism and the theme of selfdestruction. This is reflected in *Havoc*, a *roman à clef*, from 1930. After that his poetry diminished. From 1931 to 1963 he was chief literary critic of the daily newspaper *Politiken*. Ivan Opffer's drawing is from the wild years in the 1920s and carries the inscription "This is how I am, long-haired and a genius. Tom".

77

The German Occupation 1940–1945

On the morning of 9 April 1940 Denmark was occupied by German troops. Nazism did not only mean military oppression; it also embodied an ideological power which was not without attraction to some Danes. In the first months after the Occupation there was a certain influx to the Danish Nazi Party, DNSAP. Hans Scherfig's painting *The Pied Piper of Hamelin*, which is an allegory of Nazism as seducer, was painted in 1942.

Official Denmark tried as far as possible to preserve a good relationship with the occupying power. A leading spokesman for this pragmatic line was the politician Erik Scavenius, who became Foreign Minister in 1940 and Prime Minister in November 1942. The policy of cooperation was continued until 29 August 1943, when there was finally a rupture between the Government and the occupying power. For the rest of the period of occupation Denmark was without a government. The administration was continued by what was called "rule by heads of departments", which was unofficially led by the director of the Foreign Ministry, Nils Svenningsen.

Resistance was at first hesitant, and the Germans for their part strove to avoid confrontation. One of the first people to turn publicly against the occupying power was the historian

77

Dr. Vilhelm la Cour, who provoked German annoyance *inter alia* by stating in a lecture that no sensible person could seriously believe in a German victory. La Cour was imprisoned for eight months and was dismissed from his post as senior school teacher. Another early challenger of the Germans was the clergyman and writer Kaj Munk, who was liquidated by Danes working for the occupying power in 1944. The cooperation policy was seriously undermined after the German attack on the Soviet Union on 22 June 1941, when the Danish police at the request of the Germans interned a number of prominent communists and kept them in a Copenhagen prison. Some were freed, but others were sent to a camp in Northern Sealand. In 1943 the Danish Freedom Council was created to coordinate resistance groups of different political backgrounds, and at the same time links were formed with the old political parties. The relationship with the politicians was often strained and marked by clashes. In 1945, at the request of Frederiksborg Museum, Herman Vedel made a sketch of negotiations between members of the Freedom Council and leading politicians in the days just before 5 May 1945, when Denmark was liberated. This attempt to depict the events of those days as a national compromise was rejected by the Freedom Council. The result was two different paintings: Georg Jacobsen's picture of the Freedom Council and Aksel Jørgensen's large sketch of Christian X's meeting with Parliament on 9 May 1945.

Cell in *Vestre Fængsel* prison, Copenhagen

Hans Scherfig. Oil on masonite. 1941. 32 × 26.5. (A 8904).

During his detention in *Vestre Fængsel* in 1941 the writer and artist Hans Scherfig (1905–79) painted his cell on a piece of masonite with poor-quality colours. A literary description of the arrest and imprisonment of the communists is included in his novel *Frydenholm* (1962).

The Pied Piper of Hamelin

Hans Scherfig. Oil on masonite. 1942. 45.5 × 68. (A 8903).

The *Pied Piper of Hamelin* is an allegorical representation of Nazism as an ideological and moral seducer. Painted by Hans Scherfig in 1942, the year after he was arrested, with other communists, at the request of the occupying power. Scherfig was among those who were released shortly after. The picture was shown in Copenhagen in 1942. At the opening Scherfig hovered close to a rear exit in order to make a fast get-away if the Germans should put in an appearance.

77

Erik Scavenius

*Karen Trier Frederiksen.
1962. 92.5 × 73.8. (A 7554).*

As Foreign Minister during the 1st World War Erik Scavenius (1877–1962) strove to keep Denmark out of the War by means of deferring as far as possible to Germany. This "German line" made him unpopular in conservative, nationalist circles. His reputation for being particularly good at negotiating with the Germans was one of the reasons for his appointment in July 1940 as Foreign Minister. Prime Minister November 1942. His efforts to win the confidence of Germany through an active policy of adaptation brought him to a position of conflict with the feelings and opinions which were predominant among the people. After the War Scavenius was a controversial figure.

Vilhelm Buhl

*Martin Kaalund-Jørgensen.
1947. 94 × 74.5. (A 7999).*

The social-democratic politician Vilhelm Buhl (1881–1954) was Finance Minister from 1937 to 1942. With the aim of keeping the legal system in Danish hands he became a cautious supporter of the cooperation policy and a clear opponent of sabotage. Became Prime Minister after Stauning in May 1942, but resigned in November of the same year. His standing and personal integrity made him the obvious leader of the Liberation Government formed in May 1945.

Nils Svenningsen

Jørn Glob. 1970.
84.5×65.7. (A 7841).

Nils Svenningsen (1894–
1985), director of the
Foreign Ministry. The
central figure in the "rule
by heads of departments"
which prevented direct
German rule after 29
August 1943 when the
government ceased
functioning. In spite of
difficulties, it proved
possible to retain
administration in Danish
hands.

77

Kaj Munk

Jørn Glob. Pencil. 1950–51.
57.5×50. (A 7668).

The author and clergyman
Kaj Munk (1898–1944) was
the most important Danish
playwright of the period
between the Wars. His
ultimate goal was the na-
tional and Christian revival
of the Danish people. The
political developments of
the years leading up to the
2nd World War caused him
to revise his original admi-
ration for fascism; through
his poetry and drama he
fought dauntlessly against
the occupying power. He
was murdered in January
1944.

Vilhelm la Cour

August Tørsleff. 1955.
85.5×65.5. (A 7245).

The extensive historical
and archaeological works
of Vilhelm la Cour (1883–
1974) bear witness to a
strong national engage-
ment. He considered the
cooperation policy in the
first years of the Occu-
pation to be a national
disgrace. He contributed
in writing and orally to

the undermining of the cooperation policy. Imprisoned and later interned. Fled to Sweden in 1944.

The Danish Freedom Council

Georg Jacobsen. 1951–53. 242 × 391. (A 7204).

From the left, Niels Banke (1907–83), senior civil servant, member 1944; C. A. Bodelsen (1894–1978), Professor of English Language and Literature, member 1944; Mogens Fog (1904–90), Professor of Neurology, member 1943; Arne Sørensen (1906–78), writer, politician, member 1943; Aage Schoch (1898–1968), editor, director of the Danish Red Cross, member 1943; Frode Jacobsen (born 1906), M. A., member 1943; Børge Houmann (1902–94), editor, member 1943 as representative for the Danish Communist Party; Alfred Jensen (1903–88), building-worker, communist politician, member 1944; Erling Foss (1897–1982), civil engineer, member 1943; Ole Chievitz (1883–1946), physician, member 1943; Hans Øllgaard (1888–1979), Bishop of Funen, member 1944, and Erik Husfeldt (1901–84), physician, member 1945. The painting was presented to the museum in 1954 as the result of a collection raised by "the Committee for the Procurement of a painting of the Freedom Council".

78

The Resistance

Resistance began to grow in scale from 1942 onwards, and the Danish resistance movement rapidly became well organized. In the years after the Liberation much was done to keep alive memories of the activities that had contributed to the re-establishment of Denmark's esteem. Harald Essendrop's painting from 1946 of an arms-drop and Knud Raaschou-Nielsen's sabotage painting from 1945 reflect the hero-worship of the resistance which was characteristic of the years after the War. In the years 1950–51 Frederiksborg Museum asked Jørn Glob to make 19 drawings from photographs of members of the resistance who had been killed. There is also a drawing of Anders Lassen, who died serving with the British Army in Northern Italy. He was the only non-British national to be awarded the Victoria Cross in the 2nd World War. The cooperation policy had damaged Denmark's prestige in the allied countries. The contributions of a number of prominent Danes who had served with the allies helped redress this. Among them was John Christmas Møller, who was the only prominent politician to take refuge abroad in 1942. G. J. D. Bruce painted Svend Truelsen, who had turned the Danish secret intelligence service into one of the most effective in occupied Europe. After his escape to England in

78 1944 he was a central figure in SOE's Danish campaign. Aksel Jørgensen painted Henrik Kauffmann, who as Denmark's ambassador in the USA refused to receive orders from the Danish Government after 9 April 1940.

Marius Anthon Fiil

Jørn Glob. Pencil. 1950–51. 45.5 × 36. (A 7662).

Marius Anthon Fiil (1893–1944) an innkeeper and leader of the "Hvidsten Group" which participated in receiving weapons and similar actions. The group was arrested on 26 June 1944. Three days later Marius Anthon Fiil was executed together with his son, a son-in-law and five other members of the group. The six other members were sentenced to lengthy imprisonment. The contribution made by the "Hvidsten Group" and its tragic fate became a symbol of popular Danish resistance. Drawn from a photograph.

An arms-drop

Harald Essendrop. 1946.
57×80. (A 6881).

According to the artist's
information the painting
shows arms being dropped
from an English plane in
southern Sealand.

Svend Paludan-Müller

Harald Quistgaard. 1950.
Relief in terracotta.
47.3×28×4.9. (A 7647).

Colonel Svend Paludan-
Müller (1895–1944) was
head of the border guard
and cooperated with
resistance circles within
the army. Killed when
resisting German arrest.
The relief, which shows
Paludan-Müller in the
border-guard uniform,
was made posthumously
as one of several portrait-
reliefs of prominent military resistance-fighters.
The relief was made at the
Royal Porcelain factory in
Copenhagen.

78

John Christmas Møller

Otto Christensen. 1948.
54 × 40.7. (A 7360).

It was defence policy which made Christmas Møller (1894–1948) into a conservative. As leader of the *Konservative Folkeparti* from 1928 he worked to make this a centre-party with broad popular support. After 9 April 1940 he was member of the all-party government, but had to withdraw because of German pressure in October that year. He helped found the illegal newspaper *Frit Danmark*. Fled in April 1942 via Sweden to London, where he became chairman of the Danish Council. In spite of disagreement with the Freedom Council he became Foreign Minister in the Liberation Government in 1945. His opposition to moving the border in North Slesvig isolated him within his own party, which he left in 1947. Portrait donated in 1948 by the Christmas Møller Memorial Foundation.

Henrik Kauffmann

Aksel Jørgensen. 1952.
100.2 × 78.5. (A 7205).

As Danish ambassador in Washington, Henrik Kauffmann (1888–1963) refused to accept orders from the Government of occupied Denmark after 9 April 1940. In 1941 he entered into an agreement which gave the USA the right to construct bases in Greenland. His conduct strengthened Denmark's prestige among the Allies, and in recognition of his contribution he was made a member of the Liberation Government. In 1945 he represented Denmark at the San Francisco conference on the establishment of the UN.

78

Christian X's meeting with Parliament after the end of the Occupation

Aksel Jørgensen. Gouache. Composition sketch. 1955. 170 × 262. (A 7355).

The picture shows the opening of Parliament on 9 May 1945 in the *Landsting* (Upper House) Hall of Christiansborg, where Christian X in his opening speech thanked the representatives of the Allies for what the Allies had done for Denmark. The parliamentarians are standing in the Hall, while the King, seated at a table, is thanking the British General Richard Dewing. To the left of the King are Crown-Princess Ingrid and Crown-Prince Frederik (IX), to the right are Queen Alexandrine and Prince Knud. The oil painting commissioned from the sketch was never completed because of the death of the artist.

Field Marshal Montgomery being acclaimed in Copenhagen, 1945

Erik Petersen.
Press Photograph. 1945.

On 12 May the liberator of Denmark, Field Marshal Bernard Law Montgomery, arrived in Copenhagen and drove in triumph through the city.

79

Growth and welfare 1945–1965

Economic growth and the urbanization associated with it in the post-war years changed the appearance of the country. This development was observed with a sceptical eye by the artist Bo Bojesen. His drawing *Det nye Danmark* [The New Denmark] from 1962 shows the development which was in process and which became reality in the 1970s and 1980s. An essential characteristic of the first 25 years after the Liberation was the building up of the welfare state. A caricature by Bo Bojesen shows one of the political architects of the welfare state, the social democrat Viggo Kampmann. August Tørsleff painted the economist Thorkil Kristensen, Finance Minister for the *Venstre* [liberal] Party 1945–47 and 1950–53. In 1953, Erik Eriksen, as leader of the right-of-centre government, carried through a new constitution whereby a single-chamber parliamentary system came into being in Denmark. At the same time female succession to the throne was introduced. The new succession law became a symbol of women increasingly gaining ground in society as a whole. Social democrat Bodil Koch, a distinguished female politician, was Minister of Church Affairs 1953–66 and Minister of Culture 1966–68. The consolidation of the welfare state presup-

79

posed an expanding economy. August Tørsleff painted shipowner A. P. Møller, while his son and successor, Mærsk Mc-Kinney Møller, was painted by the English artist Bryan Organ. One of the Danish industrial success-stories was that of the Danfoss factory for electrical components on the island of Als, founded in 1933 by Mads Clausen.

Thorkil Kristensen

August Tørsleff.
c. 1953. 23.6×31.4.
On permanent loan from
Else Steenstrup and
Niels Peder Kristensen.

Thorkil Kristensen (1899–1989), Professor of Economics, was elected to Parliament in 1945 for the *Venstre* [liberal] Party. Became Finance Minister in Knud Kristensen's *Venstre* Government 1945–47 and in the right-of-centre coalition 1950–53. After a sensational break with his party's parliamentary group in 1959 he became Secretary General of OECD in Paris.

Text inside the image: FINANSMIN · MOTOR AFGIFT · SENSATION !!! INDEHAVEREN AF VERDENS-REKORDEN I KONTANTYDELSER · AARSPRODUKTION CA. 1.000.000.000 Kr. · KO 1959 · Bo Bojesen

The chromium-plated breed

Bo Bojesen.
Indian ink and pencil. 1959.
24.2 × 32.8. (A 13249).

The social democrat Viggo Kampmann (1910–76) was Finance Minister in 1950 and again from 1953 to 1960. Prime Minister 1960–62. The increasing tax-burden made Kampmann a much-favoured target in public polemics. But since the standard of living was also rising his popularity was not damaged. Kampmann was able in 1960 to go to the polls with the slogan "Make the good times better". The drawing shows a typical middle-class car of the Hillman type from 1959. It appeared in the daily newspaper *Politiken* on 16 June 1959 with the following text: "The forthcoming Bellahøj Agricultural Show has several surprises up its sleeve. There will be an opportunity to see Denmark's highest-yield milking".

93

79

Erik Eriksen

*Anker Hoffmann.
Limestone bust. 1973.
50×30×35. (A 7893).*

Erik Eriksen (1902–72)
grew up in a farming
environment. From 1928
until his death he ran the
farm where he was born in
Ringe on Funen. He was
Minister for Agriculture in
the Liberation Government
and in Knud Kristensen's
Government, 1945–47.

As Prime Minister and
chairman of the *Venstre*
[liberal] party he was
the architect of the new
constitution of 1953.

Aksel Larsen

*Eiler Krag. c.1963.
69.3×69. (A 8842).*

Aksel Larsen (1897–1972)
became a member of the
Danish Communist Party
as a young man. Elected
Member of Parliament in
1932, in the following
years he remained a faith-
ful party-member, loyal
to the Soviet Union. The
contribution of the Com-
munists to the Resistance
movement secured a place
for Aksel Larsen in the
Liberation Government of
1945. He was excluded
from the party in 1958 because of his criticism of the
Soviet Union's intervention
in Hungary in 1956. As
leader of the newly
founded *Socialistisk Folkeparti* (People's Socialist
Party), Aksel Larsen be-
came in the 60s a promi-
nent figure in Danish
politics.

Stephan Hurwitz

Svend Engelund. 1972.
101 x 73.4. (A 7901).

At the age of 34 Stephan
Hurwitz (1901–81) became
Professor of Law at Copenhagen University. He left
the university in 1955
when appointed by Parlia-
ment to take up the newly-
established position of
Ombudsman. In the 15
years during which he held
this post he created a central and respected place in
Danish society for the
institution of Ombudsman.

79

Bodil Koch

Anelise Søndergaard. 1965.
80.2 × 60.3. (A 7759).

Bodil Koch, née Thastum (1903–72) was a Theology graduate. She was a Member of Parliament 1947–71, Minister of Church Affairs, in various Social-Democratic-led governments, 1953–66, and Minister of Culture 1966–68. Was known for more than 30 years as an advocate, in debates on general cultural policy, of equality and of spiritual and artistic freedom.

Mærsk Mc-Kinney Møller

Bryan Organ. 1978.
101 × 76. (A 8144).

In 1940 Mærsk Mc-Kinney Møller (born 1913), son of shipowner A. P. Møller, was sent to the USA to take charge of the part of the shipping company's fleet, which was beyond the reach of the Germans; this channelled a significant amount of goodwill towards him and Denmark. As head of the A. P. Møller group he has expanded the shipping company into an international concern with activities in many fields, including oil and gas extraction in the North Sea.

Queen Ingrid

Olaf Rude. 1955.
155×106.8. (A 7359).

In 1935 Crown Prince
Frederik (later Frederik IX)
was married in Stockholm
to Princess Ingrid of
Sweden. Olaf Rude's
painting typifies a new era
of official portraiture, in
which simplified forms and
radiant colours are com-
bined with monumentality
and precisely pin-pointed
characteristics. The portrait
was commissioned by
Frederiksborg Museum and
was intended to be the
counterpart of a portrait
of Frederik IX.

80

Denmark and Europe

The 1950s and 60s were a period of economic growth without parallel in the history of Denmark. At the same time this was a period when the economy became more international, and trading across borders increased. As a result, six of Europe's industrial countries formed an economic union, in the first place based on coal and steel, but extending with the Treaty of Rome in 1957 to cover all types of commodities, including agricultural products vital to Denmark. Denmark's relationship to the E. E. C. became the main political issue of the 1960s.

One of the advocates of Danish membership of the E. E. C. was the internationally-minded social democrat Jens Otto Krag. As Foreign Minister and as Prime Minister for most of a decade he played a decisive role in the negotiations which led to Denmark joining the E. E. C. following the referendum on 2 October 1972. The day after this, the triumph of his life, Jens Otto Krag resigned as Prime Minister. At that time the E. E. C. issue had split the Danish people, however, and a breach had opened which even 20 years later had not healed, as the "No" to the European Union in the referendum of 2 June 1992 showed. The strength of the feelings evoked by the European Community is reflected in the referendum posters.

80

In terms of defence policy Denmark's allegiance was decided in 1949 with membership of NATO. In connection with this the Home Guard was established, and its prestige gained much over many years from having the respected social-democratic politician Frode Jakobsen as its commissioner.

The many protest movements of the period, including the campaign against the atom bomb, the Vietnam demonstrations and the student protests were all inspired from abroad. Victor Brockdorff painted some of the representatives of the extreme left in a large painting from the Fælled Park in Copenhagen.

Jens Otto Krag

Niels Winkel. Oil on wood. 1983.
117.5 × 159.5. (A 8593).

In this posthumous portrait the figure of Jens Otto Krag (1914–78) can be seen against the background of a painted collage of references to events in his life and political career. In addition to the newspaper article from *Berlingske Tidende*'s front page of 3 October 1972 with the headline "Denmark in the E. E. C.", the collage shows portraits of Krag when young and in middle age and a group-picture of the 4th Krag

Government, in 1971.
There are also fragments
of words which refer to
main issues in which Krag
was involved: "NORDIC",
"EFTA", "TREATY OF
ROME", and "EUROPEAN".

**"Yes" poster for the
E. E. C. referendum
of 2 October 1972**

*Hans Bendix.
Colour lithograph.
1972. 75.5 × 54.8.*

**"No" poster for the
E. E. C. referendum
of 2 October 1972**

*Colour lithograph. 1972.
71.4 × 52. On permanent
loan from the National
Museum.*

80

Frode Jakobsen

Ingeborg Borup.
Tempera on canvas.
1972. 96.9 × 95. (A 8190).

From the very first days of
the Occupation, Frode
Jakobsen (born 1906) was
an opponent of the policy
of cooperation. He was
one of the chief instigators
of the Danish Freedom
Council in 1943 and mem-
ber of the Liberation
Government. In the years
immediately after the war
he supported the European
movement, but later be-
longed to the social democrat opponents of Danish
membership of the E. E. C.
Ingeborg Borup's portrait
is clearly influenced by the
pop art of the 1960s.

The *Land og Folk* festival in the Fælled Park, Copenhagen, 1978

Victor Brockdorff. 1978–79. 172 × 251. (A 8902).

At the end of the 1960s festivals were held in many different contexts. The daily Communist newspaper *Land og Folk*, for instance, held annual festivals in the Fælled Park in Copenhagen from 1976 to 1990 in order to raise funds for the newspaper. In the foreground the writer and painter Hans Scherfig (1905–79) can be seen reading *Land og Folk*. To the left of Scherfig the artist Herluf Bidstrup (1912–88). In the background to the left of Scherfig is his wife, the artist Elisabeth Karlinsky (born 1904). Others include the trade-union leader Preben Møller Hansen (born 1929) and the theatre director and ballet-critic Allan Fridericia (born 1921), next to each other in front of the tent, and in the background, extreme right, the artist himself. Exhibited in room 81.

81

Music, literature and art after 1950

In the 1950s and 60s an active cultural policy was seen as an important element in the democratization of society. One of the results of this was the creation in 1964 of a State Fund for the Arts [officially "The Danish State Art Foundation"]. The fact that there was still a great distance between the tastes of the intellectual élite and the norms in other layers of society is reflected, however, in the criticism levelled by Peter Rindal, a storekeeper, against the state fund for the arts – criticism which has since been carried on in the form of the right-wing *Fremskridt* Party's opposition to state support of culture. In the drawing *Z-piece* Bo Bojesen comments on "Rindalism" and the cultural policy of the *Fremskridt* Party. In spite of the active state cultural policy there was still room for private patronage. In 1958 Knud W. Jensen founded the art museum Louisiana, North Sealand, which has decisively contributed to fostering interest in modern art in Denmark. The Danish Academy, founded in 1960 by twelve leading cultural personalities, was another private initiative. Among its founders was Karen Blixen, who made her home at Rungstedlund, north of Copenhagen, available for the Academy's meetings. It acquired official status when Parliament

81

funded an annual literary prize to be awarded by the Academy. The Academy's members, soon after its creation, were caricatured by Bo Bojesen. Karen Blixen and the film director Carl Theodor Dreyer, another figure of world renown in Danish cultural life, sat for paintings in the last years of their lives for the portrait collection at Frederiksborg.

In the first decade after the Liberation, the literary magazine *Heretica*, with which the most important poets of the time were linked, had notable influence. Martin A. Hansen, whose writing is sustained by ideals of a particular Nordic tradition of freedom, is an example. Other prominent members of the *Heretica* generation were Frank Jæger, Tage Skou-Hansen, Thorkild Bjørnvig and Ole Wivel. Two others, each cosmopolitan in his own way, were the bourgeois pessimist Aage Dons, painted by Tyge Bendix, and the Communist Hans Scherfig, painted by his wife Elisabeth Karlinsky. Scherfig's socially critical novels gained a readership far wider than the left-wing circles he was associated with.

Literary modernism was introduced to Denmark by the young philosopher Villy Sørensen in 1953 with *Tiger in the Kitchen and other Strange Stories*. He was painted by Hans Bendix, who also painted Tove Ditlevsen, a writer who won wide popularity both as a poet and with her novels of everyday life. The same generation produced writers such as Thorkild Hansen (*Arabia Felix*), Klaus Rifbjerg, Leif Panduro and Peter Seeberg; the last-mentioned was painted by Kjeld Heltoft.

Karen Blixen

Kay Christensen. 1955–56. 81×116.7. (A 7284).

Karen Blixen, née Dinesen (1885–1962) grew up at Rungstedlund, north of Copenhagen. From 1914 to 1931 she ran a coffee plantation in Kenya. In 1934 *Seven Gothic Tales*, written under the pseudonym Isak Dinesen, was published in New York; 100,000 copies were sold within a few months. In 1937 *Out of Africa* was published. Kay Christensen's portrait not only shows the writer's frail form and mask-like face, but also hints at the universe from which her legendary stories and fateful tales sprang.

81

Herman D. Koppel

Hans Lollesgaard.
Chalk. 1950. 22.2×19.2.
(A 13448).

The composer Herman D. Koppel (born 1908) began his career as a pianist in 1930. He taught at the Royal Academy of Music from 1949–78. Significant career as a concert pianist. In addition to piano concertos, symphonies, chamber music and oratorios, his works include music for films and theatre.

Vagn Holmboe

Helge Holmskov. Iron bust.
1976.
96×54×46. (A 7965).

Vagn Holmboe (born 1909) is one of the most important and influential Danish composers since Carl Nielsen. His works include eleven symphonies, twenty string quartets and several choral works. In addition he made a significant contribution as a teacher at the Royal Academy of Music 1950–65. Another version of Helge Holmskov's bust from 1973 can be seen in Aalborg Music Conservatory.

Z-piece

Bo Bojesen. Indian ink and pencil. 1980.
23.1×33.3. (A 13390).

In 1965 Peter Rindal (born 1923), a storekeeper, initiated a protest movement against the state fund for the arts. Later he joined Mogens Glistrup's right-wing *Fremskridt* Party (identified on voting papers by the letter "Z") and became that party's member of the state fund for the arts. Bo Bojesen's drawing of Peter Rindal in

front of Glistrup's portrait was published in 1980 with the following text: "To have a lawsuit on your hands, to be able to sort out the migrant workers' and developing countries' problems with one kick, and at the same time to enjoy trust as leader of the country's second largest party. . . THAT'S ART!"

Niels Viggo Bentzon

Anne Marie Telmányi.
1961. 88.4×73.8. (A 7751).

The immense music-output of composer Niels Viggo Bentzon (born 1919) is based mostly on his own instrument, the piano, but includes almost all genres within classical and rhythmic music. Attracted early attention for his music because of untraditional presentation/"happenings". Music critic and enthusiastic participant in public debates.

The Danish Academy

Bo Bojesen. Indian ink, pencil, water-colour and oil. 1960. 18.1×62.5. (A13170).

The Danish Academy was created on 20 November 1960. The Academy's members can be seen on Bo Bojesen's drawing, which appeared in the newspaper *Politiken* on 27 November 1960: from left to right, the writer Knud Sønderby (1909–66); the writer Karen Blixen (1885–1962); the literary critic Professor Paul V. Rubow (1896–1972); the writer Jacob Paludan (1896–1975); the literary critic Professor Hans Brix (1870–1961); the writer H. C. Branner (1903–66); the writer Tom Kristensen (1893–1974); the art historian Professor Christian Elling (1901–74); the writer Karl Bjarnhof (1898–1980); the writer Kjeld Abell (1901–61); the writer Agnes Henningsen (1868–1962), and the youngest of all, the writer Thorkild Bjørnvig (born 1918).

Hans Scherfig

Elisabeth Karlinsky. 1970s.
36 × 44.7. (A 8845).

Hans Scherfig (1905–79)
first became known for his
cheerful jungle-pictures.
He wrothe the novel *Stolen
Spring* a *roman á clef*
about a school in Copen-
hagen. From the 30s
onwards Scherfig was a
member of the Danish
Communist Party and in
travel books on Eastern
Europe and the Soviet
Union he gave enraptured
descriptions of the new
socialist world. In 1931 he
married the Austrian-born
painter Elisabeth Karlinsky.
Her portrait-sketch of her
husband dates from the
1970s.

81

Frank Jæger

Sven Havsteen-Mikkelsen.
Black chalk.
29.2×17.5. (A 8861).

Frank Jæger (1926–77) began writing at a young age in the magazine *Vild Hvede*. He achieved success with a poetry collection published when he was 22. He was an advocate of a calm life of sensual perception, far removed from the bustle and superficiality of city life. He won great popularity among the poetry-reading public and was regarded as the ideal incarnation of a poet, even becoming the model for a popular comic strip.

Villy Sørensen

Hans Bendix. 1977.
107 × 61.4. (A 8608).

The first published work of Villy Sørensen (born 1929) was *Tiger in the Kitchen and other Strange Stories*, 1953. He became involved in the debates arising from youth rebellion. His book on *Seneca* (1976) was read widely in Europe. A debate-provoking book *Oprør fra Midten* (Revolt from the Centre, written together with Niels I. Meyer and K. Helveg Petersen, 1978) placed him in the centre of the controversy over how modern societies can reach social equilibrium and ecological viability.

Tove Ditlevsen

Hans Bendix. 1964.
97.7 × 70.5. (A 7915).

The writer Tove Ditlevsen (1917–76) became known for the poetry collection *Pigesind* (A Girl's Mind) from 1939. Using as background her own Copenhagen childhood environment, which she describes in *The Secret of my Childhood* (1943), in her poems and novels she writes about universal feelings and dreams. Hans Bendix seems to have caught her in an unguarded moment, listening and smoking a cigarette in the pose of a young girl.

81

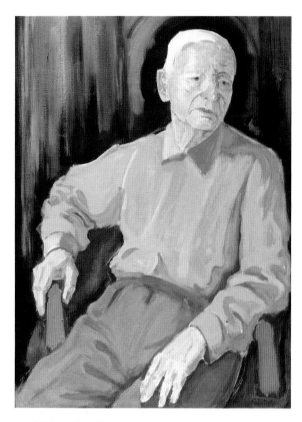

Carl Theodor Dreyer

Gunner Ditlefsen. 1967.
100.4 × 73.4. (A 7719).

Carl T. Dreyer (1889–1968)
began directing films in
1918. In the French-pro-
duced *Jeanne d'Arc* from
1928 he demonstrated his
originality. Among his
later films was *Vredens Dag*
(Day of Wrath) from 1943.
He was painted a few
months before his death.

Martin A. Hansen

Sigurd Swane. 1945.
63.5 × 55.5. (A 7410).

Martin A. Hansen (1909–55) published his first novel in 1935. This marked the beginning of a remarkable and intensive literary production, which wore the author out in 20 years. Through his opposition to Nazism in the War years he developed in his works a Christian humanism anchored in the Nordic cultural heritage. He achieved his greatest success with *The Liar* from 1950, written as radio-fiction. His other works included the novel *Lucky Kristoffer* (1945).

82

The Monarchy in the 20th century

After the transition to parliamentary constitutional practice in 1901, the monarchy was given a role independent of party politics. In 1906, at the age of 87, Christian IX died. Laurits Tuxen's representation from 1902 of the four generations, Christian IX, Frederik VIII, Christian X and Frederik IX, is strangely anachronistic. Half a century after the abolition of the ceremonial anointments, these four generations appear on the Danish throne in a grandiose composition more suitable in style for a situation of absolute monarchy. The picture is a preparatory study for a large canvas painted for the new royal palace of Christiansborg, which was built between 1907 and 1928.

Frederik VIII's period of reign proved brief. A journey he made to Iceland, which was part of the Danish kingdom until 1944, is recalled in N. V. Dorph's painting *Frederik VIII speaks on the Thingvalla plains in August 1907*. In 1912 Frederik VIII was succeeded by his son, Christian X. A highpoint of Christian X's life was the reunion of North Slesvig with Denmark in 1920. Stefan Viggo Pedersen painted the moment on 10 July when the King, on a white horse, rode over the old border. During the Occupation, 1940–45, Christian X became a national rallying figure and his daily horse-ride through Copenhagen was symbolic of the nation's will to survive. From the middle of the century the public searchlight rested to an ever-increasing degree on the king, but not only in connection with his exercise of functions of state. The everyday life of the king also became the object of general attention. The royal family appeared as the ideal nuclear family in the photograph of the royal couple and the three princesses wearing Greenland dress. King Frederik IX's interest in music is illustrated in Harald Isenstein's drawing of the King conducting. When the constitution was changed in 1953, female succession under certain circumstances was introduced. This change in the law of succession consolidated the monarchy in Denmark. Queen Margrethe II, who succeeded her father in 1972, was Denmark's first female sovereign since the Middle Ages. She is portrayed by one of the main figures of inter-national pop art, the American Andy Warhol (1986). The two bronze busts of Crown Prince Frederik and his younger brother Prince Joachim are the work of Hans Pauli Olsen. As the legal and political advisor of the sovereign, the Private Secretary to H. M. the King occupies a central position. The post has been held by a number of prominent lawyers, including A. Krieger, who held it for 26 years, 1910–36. He was loyally supportive of the royal house and played a significant role in the Easter crisis of March-April 1920, which was the only time when the monarchy was threatened in the 20th century. In 1972 Mogens Wahl, who had been Chief Officer on

82

the Faroe Islands, was nominated Private Secretary to H. M. the Queen. Niels Strøbek painted him in his official uniform at Christiansborg.

The Four Generations

Laurits Tuxen. Charcoal and water-colour. 1902. 64 × 58.5. (A 6683).

Christian IX (1818–1906) is sitting on the narwhal-tusk throne, wearing the costume of the Order of the Elephant, with his great-grandchild Prince Frederik (IX) (1899–1972). To the left, Crown Prince Frederik (VIII) (1843–1912), and to the right, Prince Christian (X) (1870–1947).

Margrethe II proclaimed Queen

Erik Petersen.
Press photograph. 1972.

On 15 January 1972, from the balcony of Christiansborg Palace, Prime Minister Jens Otto Krag proclaimed Princess Margrethe Queen of Denmark. The picture shows the Prime Minister calling for nine cheers for the new sovereign of the country.

82

King Frederik VIII

Rasmus Andersen.
Marble bust. 1908.
78 × 53 × 36. (A 1859).

Frederik VIII became king at the age of 63 in 1906. He was sympathetically inclined towards the change in the political system in 1901, and was a personal friend of the leaders of the *Venstre* [liberal] party, J. C. Christensen and Klaus Berntsen. He exercised a discreet but significant influence on foreign policy.

King Christian X

Herman Vedel. c. 1929.
45.5 × 40.5. (A 6899).

Herman Vedel's painted
sketch of Christian X is a
preparatory study for a
full-figure portrait in red
gala uniform, painted for
the Great Hall at Frederiksborg in 1929.

King Christian X's ride over the old border on 10 July 1920

Stefan Viggo Pedersen.
1920. 76.5 × 95.5. (A 2737).

In the centre of the picture
the King is riding over the
old border with a little girl,
whom he lifted up on the
horse. To the left are his
sons Crown Prince Frederik
(IX) and Prince Knud
(1900–76) on dark horses.
This painting won a prize
in a competition for the
best reunion picture.

82

King Frederik IX

Johannes Glob.
Pencil on canvas.
34.2 × 24. (A 7277).

In the 25 years between 1947 and 1972 during which Danish society underwent rapid development, Frederik IX managed to adapt the monarchy to the conditions of the new era. Outwardly the increased international communications resulted in new and demanding representation-duties for the royal couple, including state visits. Frederik IX maintained his elegant and atletic physique throughout his life.

Queen Margrethe II

Andy Warhol. Serigraphy.
1986. 97.7 x 77.7. (A 8907).

Margrethe II, when heir to the throne, married the French diplomat Count Henri de Monpezat (Prince Henrik) in 1967. The royal couple have two sons, Crown Prince Frederik and Prince Joachim. The portrait of Queen Margrethe by the American pop-artist Andy Warhol is part of a portrait-series of four "Reigning Queens" from 1986. The model for the portrait is Rigmor Mydtskov's official photograph of the Queen taken in 1972 on the occasion of the accession to the throne.

83

Science and culture after 1950

After the War the nuclear phycisist Niels Bohr had the status of a national institution. He was painted by William Scharff. In 1975, 43 years after Niels Bohr was awarded the Nobel Prize, his son, the physicist Aage Bohr, also received the prize, together with Ben R. Mottelson. They can be seen in a double portrait by Mogens Andersen. Another Danish academic scientist who made his name internationally was the astronomer Bengt Strömgren. Anders Glob painted the geologist Arne Noe-Nygaard, known as an expert on volcanoes and for his studies of the geology of Greenland. In his youth he had been a member of the Danish Freedom Council. Anders Glob also painted his father, the archaeologist P. V. Glob, State Antiquary 1960–81. Two distinguished figures in Danish cultural life were the art historian Christian Elling and the literary historian Paul V. Rubow. Haavard Rostrup, for many years a senior curator in the Ny Carlsberg Glyptotek, was a notable connoisseur of French art. Two architects who each made their mark in the public cultural debate were Steen Eiler Rasmussen and Hakon Stephensen, the latter for many years the editor-in-chief of *Politiken*.

83

Aage Bohr and Ben R. Mottelson

Mogens Andersen. 1988. 116.2 × 89.3. (A 8831).

Aage Bohr (born 1922), Professor of Physics 1956 and the third generation of the Bohr family in direct succession to hold a chair at Copenhagen University. With the American-born physicist Ben R. Mottelson (born 1926, Danish citizen 1970), Aage Bohr carried out fundamental research into the structure of the atom, leading to the Nobel Prize in Physics, 1975. The double portrait was painted at the request of Frederiksborg Museum.

Ben R. Mottelson

Ole Haupt. Photograph. 1991. 49 × 49. (F 38).

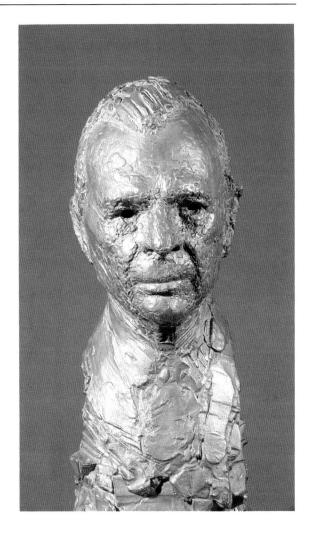

Bengt Strömgren

Knud Nellemose.
Bronze bust. 1976.
58.5 × 28 × 30.5. (A 7976).

The astronomer Bengt Strömgren (1908–86) became professor and director of Copenhagen University's Observatory in 1940. He went to the USA after the war and became professor at Princeton in 1957. On his return to Denmark in 1967 he became once again Professor of Astronomy at Copenhagen University. Pioneering work on the development of the Milky Way.

83

Christian Elling

Anne Marie Telmányi.
1967. 87.7 × 71.5. (A 7869).

Christian Elling (1901–74),
art historian, lecturer and
later professor at Copenhagen University, influenced
a whole generation of
Danish art historians. His
voluminous publications
included works on Danish
and Italian art, architecture, literature and drama.
Anne Marie Telmányi's
portrait was painted in
1967 when he retired as
professor.

P. V. Glob

Anders Glob. 1974.
100 × 80.3. (A 7900).

P. V. Glob (1911–85), professor at Aarhus University 1949 and Director of the Prehistoric Museum in Aarhus (now at Moesgård). As State Antiquary 1960–81 Glob worked for the removal of the National Museum from the inner city. Known throughout the country in the 1950s for his expeditions to the Persian Gulf. The anorak is a reference to the archaeological investigations Glob carried out in Greenland.

83

Steen Eiler Rasmussen

Knud Nellemose.
Bronze bust. 1958.
54 × 45 × 30.5. (A 8686).

The architect Steen Eiler Rasmussen (1898–1990) held the post of Professor of Architecture at the Academy of Art from 1938–68. In addition he ran his own architects' firm and made a significant contribution in the area of town planning. Author of a number of widely-read books, mostly on architecture, towns and town-development, including *London, the Unique City* (1937). Throughout his life he was an enthusiastic participant in public controversies. It is appropriate that when Knud Nellemose portrayed him, in 1985 in his 87th year, it was in the toga of a Roman sage.

Diter von Wettstein

Ole Haupt. Photograph. 1991. 49.5 × 49.9. (F 40a).

Diter von Wettstein (born in 1929), specialist in biological heredity, is one of the many foreigners who have won renown in the natural sciences in Denmark. Director of the Physiological Department of the Carlsberg Laboratory 1975. His studies of genetics gave practical results in the development of strains of barley which produce longer-lasting beer.

Eva Steiness

Marianne Grøndahl. Photograph. 1990. 45 × 56. (F 19).

The academic work of the pharmacologist Eva Steiness (born 1941) concerns the fate of medicines in the organism, their transportation in the bloodstream and later elimination. The photograph shows Eva Steiness in her laboratory in the pharmaceutical company H. Lundbeck A/S, where she is director of research.

84

The 1990s

The last decade of this century is illustrated by a selection of portraits and historic pictures combined with thematic displays which are regularly renewed as the collections are extended.

These displays can only give flickering glimpses of the times we are actually living in. One can choose to cover a broader area, or to focus on individuals, groups or events which are likely to be seen decisive. Moreover it will also be possible to study the current state of portrait art here.

84

Peter Bastian

Michael Buchwald. Photo-graph based on computer graphics. 1991.
87.8 × 60. (F 44).

Peter Bastian (born 1943), musician, was decisively influenced by the folk-music of the Balkans. As an instrumentalist he is well-known for instance as a bassoon-player with the group "Bazaar". In a widely read book on music he lays stress on the value of direct experience rather than intellectual, analytical approaches.

Rigmor Mydtskov

Pia Schutzmann. 1991.
69 × 59. (A 8942).

Rigmor Mydtskov (born 1925) was appointed Photographer to Her Majesty the Queen in 1988. Since 1962 she has had her own studio in Copenhagen. One of the best Danish portrait-photographers. The photographer's sensitively analytical and keen gaze is well-caught in Pia Schutzmann's portrait.

Henrik Nordbrandt

Bente Christensen-Ernst. 1990–91. 200 × 200. (A 8917).

Henrik Nordbrandt (born 1945) is one of his generation's most prominent poets. Many of his often melancholy poems are set in the landscapes and locations of the Mediterranean area, where he has lived for the last 25 years in voluntary exile and in a permanently unsettled state. The portrait of the author in a fez was painted in Turkey.

84

Olaf Olsen

Bjørn Nørgård. Copper-print and monotype. Printed by Niels Borch Jensen. 1993. 96.5 × 69.5. (A 8971).

Olaf Olsen (born 1928), historian, archaeologist, Viking Age specialist. As State Antiquary since 1981 he has been in charge of the rebuilding of the National Museum which has made it possible to house exhibitions of international scale there.

Per Kirkeby

A. R. Penck. Aquatint.
First half of the 1980s.
54.2 × 44.7. (A 8968).

The artist Per Kirkeby (born 1938), a geologist by training, has his background in the "Experimental Art School" at the beginning of the 1960s. Has made his name as a painter, graphic artist, sketcher, sculptor, essayist, novelist and poet, film-maker and producer; from the mid-1970s he has occupied a position of significance in the international art scene. Professor in Karlsruhe 1987, in Frankfurt from 1988. The portrait is by his friend, the German artist A. R. Penck. It contains references to Kirkeby's background as a geologist and his participation in scientific expeditions to Greenland.

137

84

Suzanne Brøgger

Suste Bonnén. Photograph.
1991. 60 × 50.5. (F 45).

Suzanne Brøgger (born
1944), author. In her
novels, she has described
the many phases of
liberation of women. The
photograph shows her in a
characteristic self-staged
pose.

Peter Schmeichel

Henrik Saxgren. Photo-
graph. 1993. 33.6 × 50.4.
(F 101).

Peter Schmeichel (born
1963), goalkeeper in the
Danish European-Cup-
winning football team in
1992. Chosen as the
world's best goalkeeper in
1992 and 1993. Kept goal
for Brøndby's UEFA-cup
semi finalists in 1991,
now plays for Manchester
United.

84

Lars von Trier

Tove Kurtzweil. Photograph. 1983.
39.4 × 32.9. (F 95).

The film director Lars von Trier (born 1956) attended the Danish Film School 1979–82. He has won various international prizes. His films include *The Element of Crime* (1982) and *Europa* (1991). His casual pose and self-confident look mark him out as an authoritative director.

Uffe Ellemann-Jensen

Marc Fluri. Photograph. 1990. 45.4×45.1. (F 49); and Anne-Marie Steen Petersen. Indian ink. 1983. 28.8×20.4. (A 13576).

Uffe Ellemann-Jensen (born 1941), graduate in Political Science, journalist. Member of Parliament for the *Venstre* [liberal] party, Foreign Minister 1982–93. Caricatured in the newspaper *Ekstra Bladet* as an absolute monarch modelled on Rigaud's portrait of Louis XIV, with the text: "Democracy, that is me!" The photograph shows the same authoritative bearing, but the year is 1990.

– Folkestyret – det er mig ! (meget frit efter Rigaud)

Index of names